RAISING THE ROOF
OF THE ROCKIES

*A Geologic History
of the Mountains
and of the Ice Age
in Rocky Mountain
National Park*

FRONTISPIECE—Trail Ridge, a remnant of the rolling upland that forms the roof of the Rockies in Rocky Mountain National Park. Originally formed 5 to 7 million years ago, it has survived despite being broken by faults, uplifted several thousand feet, cut by great canyons, and subjected to the vicissitudes of the Ice Age.

FRONT COVER (upper) — The flat top of Longs Peak, a remnant of the rolling upland, uplifted to 14,255 feet by movement along faults 5-7 million years ago.

(lower) — East face of Longs Peak, a cirque headwall excavated in the uplifted mountain by successive glaciers during the last 2 million years. The face is of granite, 1,450 million years old.

Glaciated canyon east of Longs Peak. The upper part is a spectacular example of glacial sculpture and scour. The large arcuate ridges in the lower part are end moraines deposited by the glaciers.

RAISING THE ROOF OF THE ROCKIES

By
Gerald M. Richmond

with
Graphics by
John R. Stacy
U.S. Geological Survey

Published by the

ROCKY MOUNTAIN NATURE ASSOCIATION, INCORPORATED

in cooperation with the

NATIONAL PARK SERVICE, U.S. DEPARTMENT OF THE INTERIOR

The Rocky Mountain Nature Association, Inc., is a nonprofit organization cooperating with the National Park Service in the interpretation and management of Rocky Mountain National Park.

Index map, showing the location of Rocky Mountain National Park, the Front Range, and other mountain ranges and localities outside the Park that are mentioned in the text.

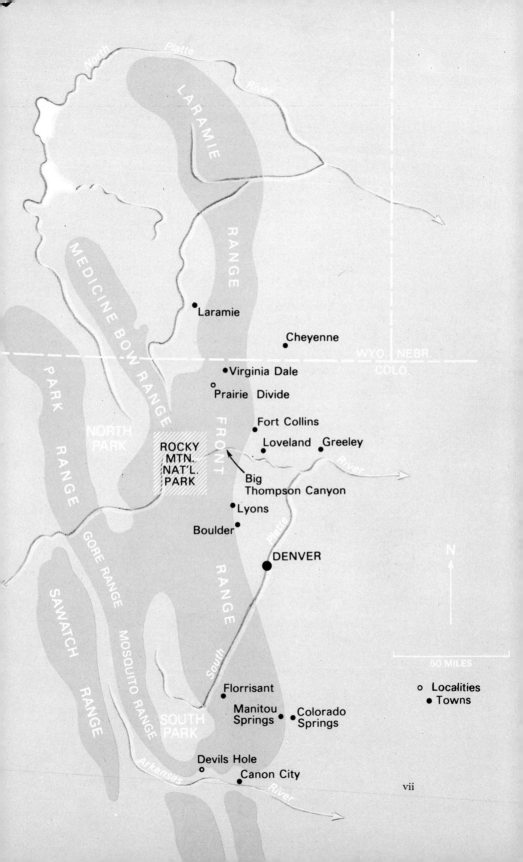

North Platte River

LARAMIE RANGE

MEDICINE BOW RANGE

PARK RANGE

NORTH PARK

FRONT RANGE

GORE RANGE

MOSQUITO RANGE

SAWATCH RANGE

SOUTH PARK

Arkansas River

South Platte

• Laramie

• Cheyenne

WYO. | NEBR.
COLO

• Virginia Dale
○ Prairie Divide

• Fort Collins
• Loveland   • Greeley

River

ROCKY
MTN.
NAT'L.
PARK

Big
Thompson Canyon

• Lyons

• Boulder

● DENVER

N

50 MILES

• Florrisant

• Manitou
Springs   • Colorado
Springs

Devils Hole
○
• Canon City

○ Localities
● Towns

vii

Preface

Driving over Trail Ridge I stopped at Forest Canyon Overlook. It was early in the day, but a few hardy souls were at the rim, their jackets buttoned and their collars turned up against the freshness of a summer morning at 11,600 feet.

"Isn't that something now!" said a young woman with her husband and two children.

"It sure is a long way down," replied the man.

"Dad! Let's go out there!" The boy started for the brink.

"Neil! Don't!" shrieked the mother and firmly grasped his arm.

They stood for a moment gazing across at the uplands of Sprague Mountain, Terra Tomah, and Mount Ida towering above the rocky canyons of Hayden Gorge and Gorge Lakes.

Casually, the girl asked, "Mom, why are the mountains so steep and then so flat on top?"

1

View from Forest Canyon Overlook. The rolling rooftops of Terra Tomah (left) and Mount Ida (right) cut by the glaciated canyon of Gorge Lakes. (Fig. 1)

"I don't know," her mother replied, "but they look like they've been there a long, long time."

"Maybe they've had a hard life," the husband laughed. "Let's go." He snapped a picture and they were off.

Two thousand feet below, the spires of a vast spruce forest ruffled the dark green floor of Forest Canyon. To the west, small blue and green lakes glittered in deep basins surrounded by high gray cliffs. Snowbanks peered from the shelter of shadows. Above the cliffs, in striking contrast, a broad, gently sloping tundra upland, the roof of the Rockies, stretched away to north and south along the Continental Divide.

The girl's question kept coming back. "Why are the mountains so steep and then so flat on top?" More questions followed. When was the flat upland formed on the mountains? Or was it perhaps formed first, and then uplifted as the mountains formed? When and how did the mountains form? The rocks must have formed first, but how much younger are the mountains? When were the canyons cut? They should be younger than the upland, which is clearly cut by their deep basin-like heads. But are they? Obviously the canyons are glaciated, for you can see ice-scoured ledges and knobs in them. But did the glaciers cut the valleys or flow down valleys that were already cut?

This geologic history of the mountains in the Park attempts to answer these and other questions. It is based on current knowledge, but future research may well prove some things wrong. That is the way science advances. The successive events are related in terms of their age, for methods are now available by which the age of certain kinds of rocks can be measured in years. Thus it is possible to say that **this** happened about 65 million years ago or **that** happened about 100 thousand years ago.

The first part of the story explores the almost incredible series of events that has brought about the present mountains. Truly, they have had a long hard life—indeed, many lives. Today, with minor exceptions, only the oldest and youngest rocks on which this history is based are preserved in the Park. To fill the gap, the intermediate history is borrowed from nearby mountains and plains (see index map), where rocks of the missing ages are preserved. You may feel skeptical, and perhaps a bit confused, as events lasting millions of years flash by in a few pages, But if the mountains seem to alternately rise and wear away faster than you can follow, pause and glance up at those in the Park. They'll still be there—and will be for millenia to come.

The second part of the story traces the events of the Ice Age—the last 2 million years—during which large glaciers advanced and receded in the canyons. Most of the landscape of the Park either is the product of sculpture and scour by these glaciers or is formed of their deposits. In fact, the shape of most features is the work of the last large glaciers which occupied the canyons from about 25,000 to about 13,000 years ago. More specific features of the landscape are mentioned and illustrated in this latter part of the story than in the earlier part, because they have survived and you can see them.

3

PART I

The Ancient Foundations

Much of Rocky Mountain National Park is underlain by rocks that are more than 1,800 million years old. These ancient rocks are chiefly gneiss and schist. They are prominently displayed in the steep headwalls of glacial basins along the Continental Divide and in cliffs along the valley walls in the central and western parts of the Park. They can be observed at close hand in rock outcrops along Trail Ridge Road. Gneiss is a light-

Banded schist and gneiss in cliffs on southeast side of Ypsilon Mountain. (Fig. 2)

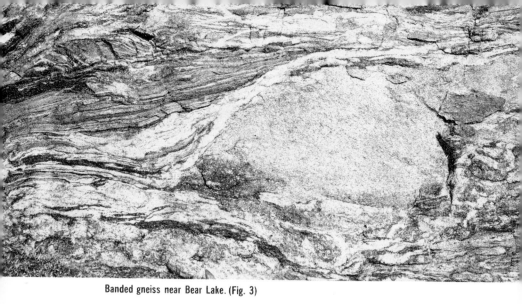

Banded gneiss near Bear Lake. (Fig. 3)

colored rock, banded in shades of black, gray, and pink. It is
made up mostly of small chunky crystals of gray quartz, pink
or gray feldspar, and a small quantity of dark minerals such as
black mica. The minerals tend to be crudely arranged in the
same direction as the banding, and give the rock a somewhat
streaked appearance. Schist is a dark-colored rock composed
mostly of shiny black minerals and a little light-colored quartz
and feldspar. A parallel orientation of the minerals is also very
noticeable in this rock. Interlayering of the dark schist and light
gneiss is common, and is easily seen in both cliffs and glacially
smoothed rock surfaces in the upper parts of the canyons.

Dark schist cut by vein of white, coarse-grained pegmatite along Fall River Pass road. (Fig. 4)

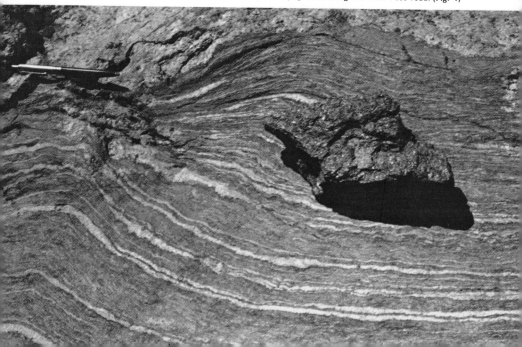

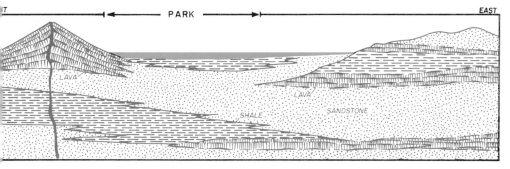

LAVA

LAVA

SHALE

SANDSTONE

Originally some of these old rocks were sediments—clays, silts, and sands—of ancient streams, lakes, and oceans. Some were of volcanic origin—probably black basalt lava flows. Together, they were many thousands of feet thick. Gradually, as they became covered by successively younger deposits, forces within the earth drew them down to depths as much as

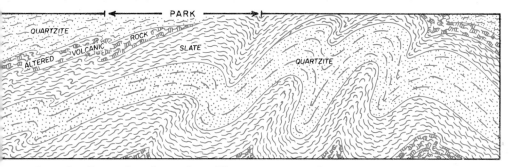

PARK

QUARTZITE

ROCK

ALTERED VOLCANIC

SLATE

QUARTZITE

5 to 10 miles under the surface. There, at tremendous pressures, and temperatures as high as 1000° F., the original sedimentary and volcanic rocks were changed by compaction, folding, and the formation of new minerals to harder rocks, like the near-vertical strata seen along the highway in Big Thompson Canyon east of the Park. Later, as we shall see, both in the Park and elsewhere in the Front Range, these rocks were further changed to become the gneiss and schist they are today.

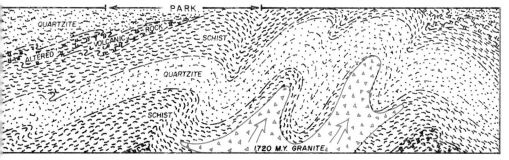

PARK

QUARTZITE

ROCK

ALTERED VOLCANIC

SCHIST

QUARTZITE

SCHIST

1720 M.Y. GRANITE

6

Granite Invasions

About 1,720 million years ago, while the ancient rocks were still deep within the earth, they were folded and changed for a second time by pressure and temperature. Simultaneously, they were invaded from beneath by a number of masses of molten rock, called magma, each a few miles in diameter. In general, these magma masses invaded parallel to the banding in the older rocks. Eventually, they cooled, crystallized, and solidified into masses of granite. Granite is a gray rock composed of chunky crystals of gray quartz, pink and white feldspar, and black mica, all easily visible. For the most part, it lacks the distinct streaky appearance characteristic of gneiss and schist. During a late phase of the cooling, mineral liquids were squeezed from between the crystals of the solidifying granite and forced out into the surrounding ancient rocks where they formed large pods and lenses parallel to the banding. Gradually, under

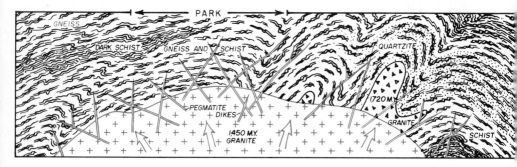

high enclosing pressures that permitted minerals to grow to a large size, they cooled and solidified into a rock known as pegmatite. Pegmatite is a light-colored rock, composed chiefly of the same minerals as granite. It differs in that the individual mineral crystals are larger, in places several inches in diameter.

About 1,450 million years ago, the ancient rocks were folded and changed by intensive pressure and high temperature for a third time. This time, they were simultaneously invaded by a very large mass of molten magma.

The margins of the invading magma tended to parallel the banding in the ancient rocks but here and there they cut across the banding. Where the pressure of the invasion shattered the surrounding rocks, the magma intruded along the fractures, widening and extending them. Blocks and fragments

7

of the ancient rocks floated off into the magma where they were partly absorbed and changed to dark clots and streaks. Along the borders of the magma the ancient rocks were similarly changed.

Gradually the magma cooled and solidified to form a large mass of granite, some 30 miles across as seen at the surface today. This granite is similar to the older one, but is lighter gray and contains larger chunky crystals of pink feldspar. From it, an intricate maze of fractures filled with granite extended outward into the surrounding rocks.

Later, the mineral liquid of the magma was forced out into fractures where it crystallized as veins of light-colored pegmatite both in the granite and in the surrounding ancient rocks whose conversion to the gneiss and schist they are today was now complete.

Granite (left) cut by coarse-grained pegmatite (right). (Fig. 5)

Both granite invasions probably pushed up the rocks above them to form mountains at the surface of the earth. How high such mountains may have been or what they looked like is unknown, for none remain. Today, after uplift and erosion of overlying rock several miles thick both granites are at the surface. The older is exposed in the mountains about 7 miles east-northeast of Estes Park. It also forms the hills east of Grand Lake and Shadow Mountain Lake in the western part of the Park. Southeast of the Park, it is exposed in the canyon of North St. Vrain Creek, along the highway west of Lyons. The younger light-gray granite forms the mountains north and south of Estes Park, Estes Cone and Twin Sisters. It forms Hagues Peak to the north and is spectacularly displayed in the east face of Longs Peak. A gently sloping contact between the granite and the older overlying gneiss and schist can be seen in cliffs along canyons east of the Continental Divide, where also light-colored pegmatite veins extend in all directions through the gneiss and schist. All these rock types can be observed at close hand along trails in these areas.

A Great Hiatus

From about 1,450 million years ago to about 530 million years ago almost nothing is known of the geologic history of the Park. To the south, a third granite, of which Pikes Peak is formed, invaded the ancient rocks of that region about 1,050 million years ago. But in the northern Front Range there is a great hiatus, or gap, in the record. Possibly, a prominent band of black basalt, known in the Park as the "Iron Dike," intruded along a fracture in the older rocks during this time. The dike, several yards wide, cuts vertically across these rocks in a south-easterly direction from Mount Chapin nearly to the Longs Peak Ranger Station. It can be seen easily along Trail Ridge Road below the crossing of the ski lift, in the bank of the Big Thompson River at "the Pool" near the crossing of the Fern Lake Trail, and in Storm Pass along the trail northwest of Estes Cone.

9

At least the latter part of the long hiatus is thought to have been chiefly a time of extensive erosion. It is known that by about 530 million years ago, central Colorado had been reduced to a nearly featureless plain at sea level, for a sea deposited sands (now sandstone) of this age over an essentially flat terrain eroded across the old gneisses, schists, and granites. Exposures of the sandstone resting on granite can be seen in the canyon west of Colorado Springs.

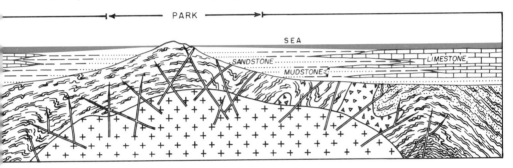

The Era of Shifting Seas

From about 530 million years ago to perhaps 300 million years ago, central Colorado was invaded by relatively shallow inland seas which alternately spread across and receded from the region. Rocky Mountain National Park was probably covered by some of these seas, but not by others. None of their deposits remain in the Park today, but remnants of them have been found about 50 miles to the north, near Virginia Dale. They are well exposed at Manitou Springs in the canyon west of Colorado Springs, and elsewhere farther west in Colorado.

The deposits of the seas are mostly sandstone, limestone, and shale; and the life that roamed the seas included such creatures as trilobites, sharks, and fishes, as well as many varieties of shellfish such as clams, snails, and brachiopods. All the species living at that time are now extinct, but their shells or bones remain as fossils in the rocks of that era.

Trilobite

Brachiopod

10

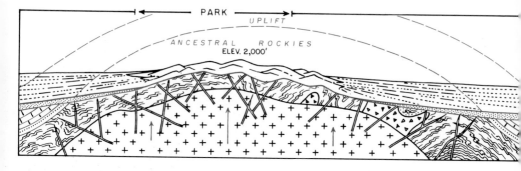

The Ancestral Rockies

About 300 million years ago the region of the present Front Range, including the Park, was uplifted from the seas. Immediately, streams began to erode away the previously deposited marine sediments. As the land rose higher, the streams cut through the sediments and deeply into the underlying older granite, gneiss, and schist. They stripped away all of the marine rocks, about 300 feet thick, and 2,000 to 3,000 feet of the older rocks. Eventually, a range of mountains, the Ancestral Rockies, was sculptured in the uplifted land mass. Though the total uplift of the land may have amounted to 4,000 to 5,000 feet, the pace of erosion was such that the mountains were never that high. Summits in the area of Rocky Mountain National Park were perhaps 2,000 feet above seas only about 100 miles distant to east and west. The debris carried from the mountains by the streams was spread on broad, gently sloping plains that fanned out to the seas. It was on these plains that air-breathing forms of life—amphibia —first developed in this region.

An early amphibian

PARK

DUNES ELEV. 500' DUNES SHALLOW SEA

March of The Dunes

By about 240 million years ago the mountains had been reduced to low hills, and the plains to east and west were overrun by widespread coastal sand dunes which encroached over the land in front of an advancing shallow sea. It was at this time that reptiles first appeared. The dunes and sea ultimately spread across the region north of the Park, but probably did not cover the Park itself.

Then, about 190 million years ago, renewed uplift of the land caused the sea to recede again, and, following its shores, marched the coastal dunes. The dune sands and the deposits of the sea are now preserved as sedimentary rocks along the edges of the mountains east of the Park.

Dragons of The Flood Plains

Following the retreat of the dunes, broad tropical plains dotted with lakes and swamps spread out along major drainage ways from low mountains in the area of the Park. This time was the middle of the Age of Reptiles when dinosaurs, both large and small, abounded. The deposits of these flood plains, now rocks, constitute the famous Morrison Formation in which so many large dinosaur skeletons, such as those in Dinosaur National Monument, have been found. The formation is named from the little town of Morrison, west of Denver, near which exposures of the formation in a deep highway cut are preserved as a special exhibit.

Allosaurus, a carnivorous dinosaur

Brontosaurus, a herbivorous dinosaur

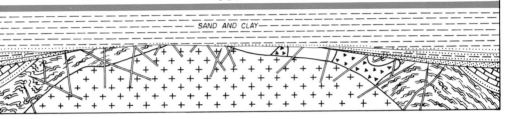

The Last Seas

Eventually the sea began to encroach over the region again and, by about 100 million years ago, it had covered most of the Park, where it remained for more than 30 million years. Thousands of feet of sand and clay (now sandstone and shale) and some calcareous sediment (now limestone) were successively deposited on its floor, buried, forced down into the earth, and solidified into rock. Life in the sea included ammonites whose shells evolved through a remarkable series of coiled forms with the passage of time. Finally, about 70 million years ago, the sea withdrew from Rocky Mountain National Park and has never returned. Outcroppings of shale, probably deposited about 75 million years ago, have been found in the saddle east of Lead Mountain in the northwest part of the Park. The sea withdrew gradually, taking about 16 million years to leave all of Colorado.

Didymoceras stacyi, an ammonite

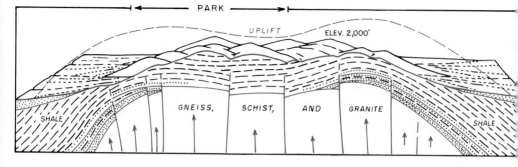

The Rockies Begin to Rise

The sea withdrew because the crust of the earth was being forced upward. This upward force caused the ancient foundation rocks to break along steep fractures into great blocks which were uplifted irregularly in a north-trending region that is now the Front Range of Colorado and includes the Park. The previously deposited sediments, now rocks, were stretched into broad folds across the irregularly rising blocks. Eventually the sedimentary rocks broke along the western side of the uplift, near the present west boundary of the Park, and great masses of the granite and gneiss core of the mountains spread or slid slowly westward over younger rocks toward lower terrain.

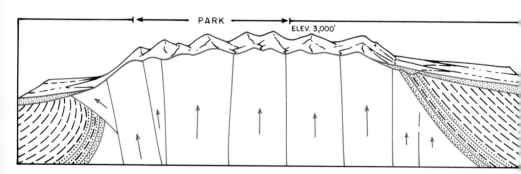

At the surface, streams attacked the slopes of the land as it rose from the sea, stripping away the soft marine deposits. About 68 million years ago volcanoes broke out in the Front Range south of the Park, and volcanic ash from them blew into the receding sea. There it was buried in the deposits where it is now preserved as layers of bentonite. After the sea had withdrawn from Colorado, streams carried large quantities of

15

silt and clay east and west to great swampy plains on which flourished a luxuriant subtropical vegetation destined to become bituminous coal.

By about 67 million years ago the streams had eroded away nearly 5,000 feet of sedimentary rocks from the mountains and had cut into the underlying ancient gneiss, schist, and granite. They deposited the eroded material on broad plains along the foot of the mountains. At that time, summit areas were perhaps as much as 3,000 feet above sea level and rose 2,000 to 2,500 feet above the surrounding lowlands. It was on these flood plains that the last of the dinosaurs, the great three-horned Triceratops, died out about 65 million years ago. Bones of these large reptiles have been found in deposits of this age near Greeley, east of the Park.

Triceratops

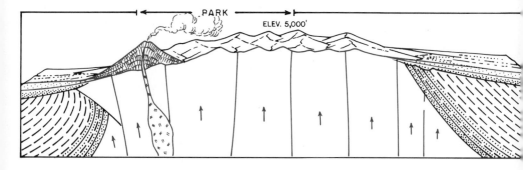

And Rise Some More

From about 65 million years ago to about 54 million years ago continued uplift raised the mountains to greater heights. Each upward pulsation invigorated stream erosion on a grand scale. About 54 million years ago volcanoes broke out again in the Front Range. One of these erupted in the Park, in the area of the present east and south slopes of Mount Richthofen. Here the remains of lava flows, composed of a volcanic rock called andesite, rest on the ancient gneiss and schist; and a plug of similar andesite, formed in the throat of the volcano, appears to cut through the deposits of the last seas.

The mountains at this time were possibly 4,000 to 6,000 feet above sea level, though the summits of the volcanoes were probably a few thousand feet higher. To the north in southeastern Wyoming, the Laramie, Medicine Bow, and Park Ranges were also highlands, from which streams carried gravel and sand into adjacent broad lowland basins. It was in the warm humid, temperate to subtropical forests of these lowlands that small mammals developed, among them the tiny horse, Hyracotherium, commonly called Eohippus.

Eohippus

17

ELEV. 2,000' ELEV. 3,500' ELEV. 2,000'

|← PARK →|

WEATHERING

Erosion Gains Control

Throughout the uplift and volcanism, the region of Rocky Mountain National Park was being eroded. The erosion continued until about 40 million years ago, by which time the mountains had been reduced to low hills. Summits where the Continental Divide is now were probably only a few hundred feet above adjacent valleys. The hilly terrain blended eastward into a gently rolling plain on which some major streams established courses in nearly the same positions as those they occupy today.

Reddish, deeply weathered granite along road up Deer Ridge, about one mile north of Beaver Meadows entrance. (Fig. 6)

Rounded core of weathered granite along Colorado Highway 66, one-quarter mile southwest of Estes Park. (Fig. 7).

Though no deposits of this long interval of erosion have been found in the Front Range, weathering — that continuous breaking up and decay of rocks to produce soil — was extraordinarily deep on the ancient plain. Even now, more than 40 feet of reddish weathered rock is preserved on it in places. The weathered rock falls apart easily, though many of the mineral grains are little decayed chemically. In the lower part of the decayed zone, the weathering process worked its way down into the blocky network of fractures in the underlying rock. As the sides of the blocks disintegrated, their unweathered cores remained as round masses of fresh rock surrounded by weathered debris. Later, when erosion stripped away this debris, the round cores were left behind as giant boulders which either remained in their original position or tumbled down the slope. Such boulders, easily mistaken for glacial boulders, are widespread on the knobs and mountains north of Estes Park, and the crest of Lumpy Ridge may be a remnant of the ancient plain. As we shall see, parts of the plain north and northeast of the Park were later covered by younger deposits for long intervals of time, and then exhumed as the covering rocks were stripped away by erosion. This accounts for the survival of the plain in places. Whether or not the gently sloping tundra uplands on Trail Ridge and along the Continental Divide are remnants of this plain has long been debated by geologists, but the available evidence indicates that they are of much younger origin.

19

No stream deposits of this long erosion interval have been found in the Front Range, but fossil leaves and tree pollen preserved in deposits of silt and volcanic ash of this age in south-central Colorado and in Wyoming show that the forest changed progressively from its earlier subtropical character to an open savannah with groves of palm trees about 49 million years ago. Subsequently, it changed to a warm humid forest of broad-leaved evergreens and subequatorial hardwoods; then to a dry tropical forest of mixed hardwoods; and finally to a hardwood forest with open grassland parks, and brush and pine at higher elevations. These changes show that the climate became increasingly drier.

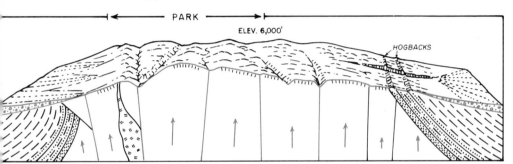

The Mountains Rise Again

About 40 million years ago, forces within the earth again uplifted the northern part of the Front Range, including the Park. In central Colorado, to the south, the uplift was probably only a few hundred feet. Following it, the region west of Pikes Peak was at an altitude of only about 3,000 feet. In Wyoming, to the north, the uplift was over 1,500 feet in places and the mountains were probably at altitudes of 5,000-6,000 feet. As the mountains rose, the surface of the former widespread plain was tilted upward so that it sloped away from them more steeply.

Hogback ridge west of Lyons. Layers of former sand dunes changed to rock have been tilted upward by the rising mountains and eroded by streams to form the ridge. (Fig. 8)

Erosion accompanied the uplift, cutting valleys in the old rocks of the mountains. On their flanks it etched away the soft sedimentary rocks from between the harder sandstone layers which remained behind as "hogback" ridges at the base of the mountains. These can be seen along the highway east of the Park at Lyons, at the mouth of Big Thompson Canyon west of Loveland, and along the highways north and west of Fort Collins. Erosion was greatest along major streams. In the Park, the ancestral Colorado River eroded a canyon at least 1,000 feet deep at La Poudre Pass, and another ancient stream, possibly tributary to the ancestral Colorado, cut a canyon 1,000 feet deep at Milner Pass.

In places, especially in Wyoming, mountains were uplifted across the path of major streams, but so slowly that the streams were able to cut their channels down as fast as the land rose. Thus, little by little they entrenched themselves in canyons across the mountains. Some of these canyons were nearly 1,500 feet deep. To the south, in central Colorado, major streams eroded valleys only about 200 feet deep at this time.

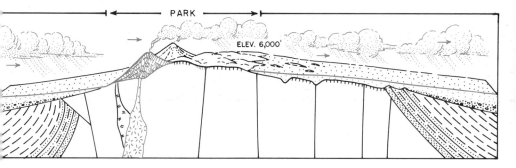

ELEV. 6,000'

PARK

Neck Deep in Volcanic Ash

From about 37 million years ago to about 34 million years ago, volcanic ash, borne by the winds from volcanoes to the southwest and west, engulfed the basins on both sides of the northern Front Range and filled the canyons in its flanks. Although the mountains in the Park, still about 6,000 feet above sea level, probably were not covered, the somewhat lower mountains north and northwest of the Park were nearly buried. Patches of the ash remain today on some summit areas in the Medicine Bow and Laramie Ranges in Wyoming.

At about the same time, volcanoes broke out west of Canyon City in the southern part of the Front Range. Lava and hot volcanic ash flows spread out from them across the deeply weathered surface of the former widespread plain. Remnants of the lava on the weathered surface of the plain still can be seen in Devils Hole along the Arkansas River.

The climate of this interval was warm-temperate to subtropical, as indicated by the presence of leaves and pollen of many broad-leafed trees and sequoia in lake deposits of this age at Florissant, west of Colorado Springs. Ponderous titanotheres and rhinoceroses roamed both mountains and plains, as well as many small rodents such as rabbits, beavers, opposums, cat-like and dog-like carnivores, and dog-sized three-toed horses. The particular species are now extinct.

Brontotherium, a titanothere

Specimen Mountain And
The Lulu Mountain Volcano

North of the Park, Lulu Mountain is the remains of a somewhat younger volcano which broke out about 28 million years ago in association with steep fracturing of the earth's crust along the west side of the Front Range. Specimen Mountain has long been considered to be the remains of a similar volcano. It is formed of layers of volcanic ashflow rock, obsidian, mudflows, volcanic debris fallen from the air, and lava flows of a kind known as rhyolite. These different kinds of rocks can readily be seen along the trail up Specimen Mountain.

Recently, however, R. B. Taylor has discovered that the volcanic ashflow rock and underlying obsidian which cap Specimen Mountain and adjacent summits actually are deposits of a volcanic ashflow, which erupted as a dense cloud from another volcano or caldera, possibly to the northwest, and spread rapidly across the area of Specimen Mountain, where it collapsed, and welded into rock while still hot. The phenomena is somewhat analogous to the ash eruption of Mount Vesuvius that destroyed Pompeii. Moreover, the fact that the ashflow deposit caps Specimen Mountain and adjacent summits shows that Specimen Mountain could not have been an active volcano at the time of the ashflow eruption 28 million years ago.

Volcanic debris fallen from the air, exposed along trail up Specimen Mountain. (Fig. 10)

However, volcanoes existed at Lulu Mountain and probably elsewhere. A granite-like rock, formed from molten magma that congealed at depth in the source chamber which fed the vocanoes, is exposed in the area of Michigan Lakes and along the ridge from Mount Richthofen to a point south of Lead Mountain. The volcanoes probably formed large cones, above the surrounding terrain, and may have attained altitudes of 8,000 to 10,000 feet above sea level. The materials that erupted from them filled the deep canyons at Milner Pass and La Poudre Pass, and are spectacularly exposed in the Little Yellowstone headwaters of the Colorado River southeast of La Poudre Pass. To the west they overlapped the deeply eroded remains of lava flows from the 54-million-year-old volcano on Mount Richthofen. To the east they flowed out over a rugged terrain eroded in the ancient gneiss, schist, and granite. At Iceberg Lake on Trail Ridge, an ashflow, possibly the same as that on Specimen Mountain, filled a steep-walled valley at least 500 feet deep. The welded ashflow rock can be seen in the cliff above the lake; to the north and south the old walls of the valley filled by the ashflow rock are of gneiss.

Volcanic rocks in cliff south of Specimen Mountain. Upper part is volcanic ashflow with black obsidian layer at base. Middle part is gray tuff and rhyolite lava flows. At bottom, almost out of sight, are stony mudflow deposits and fragmental volcanic debris that fell from the air. The basin beneath the cliff is not "the crater" of a volcano, as it has been mistakenly named. (Fig. 9)

Volcanic ashflow cliff at Iceberg Lake. The ashflow fills a valley cut in the ancient gneiss which is exposed on upland to right and left. (Fig. 11)

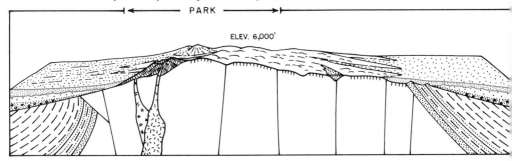

Waist Deep in Volcanic Sand And Silt

About 26 million years ago, streams began again the never-ending process of erosion, transport, and deposition. They carried large quantities of debris from the volcanoes and from other uplands in the Park down to the surrounding valleys and lowlands where they deposited it, along with volcanic ash blown in from active volcanoes to the west. Some of these deposits can be seen in the large roadcuts along the highway leading south from the Park, west of Grand Lake. There, they consist of layers of tan sand and silt eroded from nearby uplands, such as Specimen Mountain, together with some layers of white volcanic ash.

25

Layers of volcanic sand, silt, and ash along Colorado Highway 34, south of Grand Lake Junction. (Fig. 12)

North of the Park, in southern Wyoming, the streams deposited such large quantities of these sediments that the lowlands were eventually filled. Low mountains such as the Laramie Range were buried again and higher mountains were more extensively covered than they had been by the volcanic ash 34 million years ago. In Colorado, the still higher Front Range, including the Park, was not covered but remained an area from which sediments were eroded.

This was a time when mammals developed rapidly. Small pony-sized horses, camels, pig-like oreodonts, and rhinoceroses thrived, and were eaten by carniverous beasts such as bear-like, fox-like, and wolf-like dogs. Cats were also predators; some had long stabbing teeth, and others were ancestral to your tomcat. Mountain forests were predominantly of pine with sparse spruce and fir, and a few broad-leafed trees such as elm and hickory. In the lowlands were brushy grassland parks and broad-leafed forests.

An oreodont

26

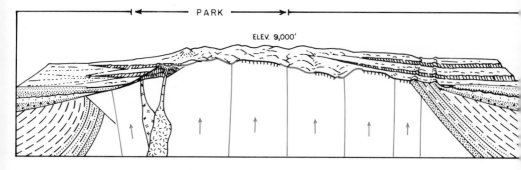

Uplifted, Exhumed, And
Awash in Their Own Debris

At some time about 18 million years ago uplift began again to intermittently raise the mountains of northern Colorado and southern Wyoming. Streams stripped away most of the cover of volcanic sediments and ash which they had previously deposited. Many tended to find their former courses and to partly or wholly re-excavate their old valleys and canyons in the flanks of the mountains.

From the edge of the mountains, the streams fanned out across broad, gently sloping plains to surrounding lowlands. Beyond to east and north, major rivers eroded valleys 200 to 300 feet deep. To west and south, however, no valley erosion appears to have taken place.

As erosion of the mountains progressed, the streams at lower elevations began to fill again the valleys and canyons they had just excavated. At first their deposits contained many boulders and cobbles, which were carried far out from the mountains. Later, they became chiefly sand and silt mixed with volcanic ash. This filling continued until 5 to 7 million years ago, by which time the mountains north of the Park in Wyoming were almost completely buried. Streams flowed east from the Park Range across the crests of the Medicine Bow and Laramie Ranges to the highest surface of the High Plains. West of Cheyenne, stream deposits of this age, as well as the older volcanic sand and ash, still extend up onto the summit of the Laramie Range, and their gently sloping surface is utilized by both railroad and highway as the easiest route onto the mountains. Elsewhere, they still fill or partly fill many ancient valleys and canyons.

27

In northern Colorado, northwest of the Park, valleys were filled to within about 1,000 feet of the highest summit areas. In central Colorado, south of the Park, they were filled to a much less degree. East of the Park, it is difficult to determine just how far up onto the mountains the filling extended because so few of the deposits remain today and because this area has been uplifted here and downdropped there by subsequent faulting.

The climate during this time of canyon filling became increasingly dry, but was still more humid than today. Mountain forests were chiefly pine, with a few hardwoods such as elm and birch. Spruce, fir, and pine grew at higher elevations, sagebrush at lower elevations. Animal life in the lowlands included the first one-toed horses, pliohippus, as well as rodents, three-toed horses, mastodons, rhinoceroses, and many camels.

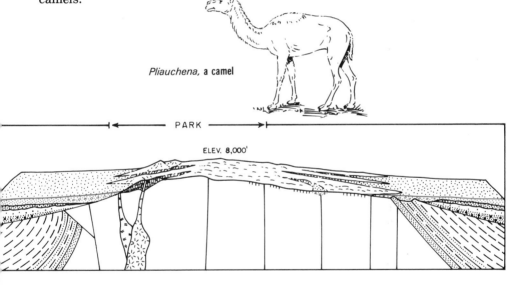

Pliauchena, **a camel**

PARK

ELEV. 8,000'

The Flat-topped Uplands

The material carried by the streams during the time of canyon filling was eroded from the mountains. Gradually these mountains were worn away until the summit areas in the Park became a region of rounded hills and ridges, at an altitude of about 8,000 feet, which rose 500 to 1,500 feet above broad valleys that sloped gently east and west to the edge of overlapping stream deposits. To the east the surface probably

Gently sloping upland extending across ashflow rock and gneiss along Trail Ridge Road above Iceberg Lake.(Fig. 13)

merged imperceptibly in places with the deeply weathered surface of that ancient plain formed about 40 million years ago and, farther east, with the surface of the stream deposits filling the canyons and extending eastward onto the High Plains. This ancient scenery may be visualized from Trail Ridge (see frontispiece) and many other summit areas, if you look out over the gently sloping uplands and imagine that the deep canyons are not there. The highest hills were where they are today — along the Continental Divide, along Trail Ridge, and in the Mummy Range. The broad intervening valleys were where the canyons are now. The region as a whole, however, was about 4,000 feet lower than today.

The summit uplands, though flat in contrast to the present canyon walls, are not actually flat, as any hiker can testify. Some, such as Bighorn Flats, slope as little as 300 feet per mile; but most slope at about 600 feet per mile, or about 1 inch per step. In places, as between Andrews Pass and Taylor Peak, the slope is 1,000 feet or more per mile. The steepest terrain was probably in the Never Summer Mountains and north of the Park, where the high volcanoes were being destroyed by erosion.

It is logical to ask why the gently sloping uplands might not be actual remains of that deeply weathered 40-million-year-old plain. Proof that the summit uplands in the Park are not a part of that plain can be seen at Iceberg Lake on Trail Ridge Road. There, as we have seen, a volcanic ashflow, only about 28 million years old, fills a former valley in the ancient gneiss. The gently sloping upland extends without interruption across the gneiss, across the tops of the buried valley walls, and across the ashflow rock. The surface of the upland, therefore, must be less than 28 million years old, and not a part of the 40-million-year-old plain. For the last 5 to 7 million years it has remained the roof of the Rockies, enduring with little modification the vicissitudes of subsequent uplifts, faulting, stream erosion, and glacial climate.

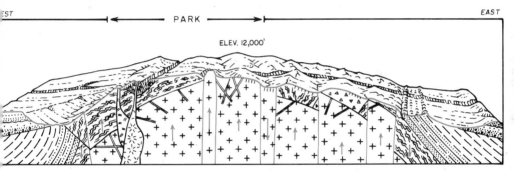

Ups and Downs

About 5 to 7 million years ago, forces within the earth initiated a final broad uplift of the Rocky Mountain region. This was accomplished chiefly by renewed movement along old faults, though in many places opposite to the original movement. Some mountains were uplifted; others collapsed. In like manner, some lowland areas were downdropped and others uplifted. In the Park, the overall effect was to raise the mountains as much as 4,000 to 5,000 feet, which brought the summits to their present altitudes above 12,000 feet. As during previous uplifts, this uplift was uneven and the region was broken by steep fractures, or faults, along which adjacent parts of the mountains were raised or lowered with respect to each other.

The down-dropped basin of Estes Park. One fault, along which movement took place, lies along the foot of the mountains across the basin. View is northeast from Deer Mountain. (Fig. 14).

The displacements tended to be greatest along the flanks of the mountains, although some large displacements occurred within them. However, in many places the offset of adjacent mountain blocks was only a few tens or hundreds of feet. Because Rocky Mountain National Park has not been geologically mapped in detail, the location of such faults and the amount of displacement of mountain blocks adjacent to them are not known.

Movement of the mountain blocks displaced the land surface up or down. Trail Ridge and other parts of the flat-topped upland along the Continental Divide were clearly uplifted. The small, flat summit of Longs Peak appears to have been uplifted some 800 feet higher. The basin of Estes Park may have been downdropped as much as 1,000 feet. Remaining areas of the deeply weathered 40-million-year-old plain were also broken and uplifted or downdropped, so that its original relation to the younger flat-top upland is difficult to determine.

31

As the mountains were jostled up and down, the ability of streams to erode or deposit was greatly changed. Probably some valleys were broken and offset up or down by the movement. Streams formed waterfalls where they flowed across a fault scarp from an uplifted area to a downdropped area. An abrupt change in gradient of canyons in the east flank of the Front Range may have originated in this way. Streams whose courses were blocked by an uplifted mass formed temporary lakes or were forced to turn sharply along the fault to find a new outlet. The great bend in the canyon of Tonahutu Creek at Big Meadows may have such an origin.

Deep Erosion

Despite the temporary derangement of the streams, the net effect of the broad uplift of the region was to increase erosion both in the mountains and throughout the regions to east and west. To the north, in Wyoming, the mountains were exhumed; to the south, in central Colorado, deep canyons were cut. In the Park, the shallow valleys extending away from the Continental Divide and the crest of the Mummy Range were deepened, and eventually became winding V-shaped canyons 600 to as much as 1,500 feet deep. The Colorado River to the west, the Cache La Poudre River to the north, and the Big Thompson River to the east all cut deep canyons, in places exhuming former canyons which they had previously filled. Lesser streams stripped away almost all of the older overlapping sediments—though some remain in a few places, as at Prairie Divide northwest of Fort Collins. Where the mountains meet the plains, the hogback ridges were again exposed. Even on the plains, rivers such as the South Platte cut broad valleys 600 to 1,000 feet deep. It was a period of great erosion.

PART II

The Ice Age Cometh

For the past 2 million years or so the earth's climate has alternated from cold periods to warm periods, each lasting many thousand years. What has caused these climatic changes? Many scientists believe that they have resulted from fluctuations in the amount of heat which the earth receives from the sun. The fluctuations are thought to be caused by variations in the amount of eccentricity, or off-centeredness, of the earth's orbit around the sun.

It is also known that the amount of heat received from the sun may be affected by changes in the earth's atmosphere. For example, a time of world-wide increase in the amount of carbon dioxide or volcanic dust in the atmosphere would prevent some of the sun's heat from reaching the earth's surface. The relative importance of these different possible causes is not understood. However, their total effect has been alternately to cool the oceans and cause large continental icecaps and mountain glaciers to form at some times, and to warm the oceans and cause the glaciers to waste away at other times. Alternation of cold- and warm-water shells at successive depths in ocean sediments, and alternating layers of glacial deposits and interglacial soils on the continents show that this has happened several times in the last 2 million years. This series of climatic changes is called the Ice Age or the Quaternary Era. Thought until recently to have included four or possibly five times of widespread glaciers, it is now believed by some to have consisted of more, the precise number being still undetermined. Each glaciation included several secondary advances and recessions of the ice.

What Is a Glacier?

In early summer, snow still covers much of the high country in Rocky Mountain National Park. Gradually it disappears until, by late August, the small amount remaining is mostly on the upper parts of small glaciers nestled at the foot of high cliffs. Snow is the life blood of glaciers; they cannot develop or grow without it. Whether snow will remain throughout the summer depends on the amount of snow accumulated in winter and on summer temperatures.

Andrews Glacier, showing long ridge of accumulated névé formed by snow blowing over the crest.
(Fig. 15)

In July though the temperature may be over 100° at the airport, a plane, as it climbs will be in colder and colder air until, at some altitude, it passes through air that is at freezing temperature (32° F.) into air that is below freezing temperature. Mountains that rise above the average altitude of summer freezing temperature have glaciers on their summit uplands if enough snow accumulates. The average altitude of freezing temperature in summer over Rocky Mountain National Park is about 14,800 feet. This is more than 500 feet above Longs Peak and some 2,000 feet above most other peaks. Therefore, under present conditions of snowfall, glaciers cannot form on the summit uplands in the Park. Were it not for the high cliffs along the Continental Divide there would be none at all. These cliffs, acting like snow fences, cause snow blowing off the uplands to fall in the basins beneath. This greatly increases the accumulation of snow in the basins during the winter. Andrews Glacier, today, well exemplifies this process. In summer, the cold shadows of the cliffs protect the snow sufficiently so that some lasts from year to year to nourish the existing small glacier.

How does snow become glacial ice? As snow accumulates, the pressure of individual flakes against each other causes them to recrystalize into tiny crystal granules. During times of thaw, especially in summer, melt-water from the upper layers infiltrates and refreezes in the granules beneath, causing them to grow. As granules come in contact, adjustment in growth takes place, controlled by the pressure of granules against one another, until all granules are about equal in size. This process is completed in a single season, and the resulting mass of granular snow is known as névé (pronounced nevay). Old gray névé of past summers can often be seen protruding from beneath younger whiter snow at the head of a glacier.

As a layer of névé is buried by an increasing thickness of younger névé and surface snow, it compacts, forcing the air out from between the granules. These continue to grow until, when all are completely in contact and all of the air except for a few bubbles has been expelled, the mass is solid ice. This process may take only a few years or as long as 20 to 30 years, and is completed under a cover of snow and névé as much as 100 feet thick.

Névé exposed above ice of Rowe Glacier (1923). (Fig. 16)

Ultimately the weight of the snow, névé, and ice exerts sufficient stress to cause the lower part of the ice to begin to flow downslope in the same way that a plastic flows. Flow is fastest in the central part of a glacier. It is slower in the lower part because of friction against the ground. The upper 200 feet or so of a glacier does not flow. It rides on the underlying flowing ice and breaks under stress to form crevasses; for example, where a glacier flows over a cliff in a valley floor. At the front it may shear upward and be thrust over itself by the pressure of the flowing ice behind it. At the head of a glacier, the ice tends to pull away from its rock headwall, opening a deep arcuate crevasse known as a bergschrund.

36

Bergshrund at head of Tyndall Glacier (1947). (Fig. 17)

Glaciers, like snowbanks, melt and evaporate in summer. Water runs both down their surface and beneath them, and flows from their fronts. During the warm summers of the 1930's and 1940's, glaciers melted and evaporated so much that their fronts receded considerable distances and their surfaces were noticeably lowered. Throughout this time, however, the ice of each glacier continued to flow forward. Glacier fronts recede when melting and evaporation are greater than the forward flow of the ice. Glacier fronts advance when melting and evaporation are less than the forward flow. Which may happen is forecast by changes in the year-to-year position of the névé line, the lower limit of the névé on a glacier in late summer. When the névé line becomes lower in successive years, the glacier is building up its ability to grow; when the névé line recedes headward in successive years, the glacier is losing its ability to grow.

37

What a Glacier Does

Before the first glaciers formed, the few cliffs along the Continental Divide were mostly at the heads of sinuous V-shaped canyons cut by streams during the time of deep erosion, 2 to 5 million years ago. The first lasting snows accumulated in these valley heads. Snowbanks are by nature more or less elliptical in outline. Summer meltwater saturates the ground under them and the seepage from their lower margins causes the soil to flow or be washed from beneath them. In this way, soil was removed gradually from beneath the first snowbanks until they lay on rock in broad elliptical basins which, though shallow, were deep enough to permit formation of the first glaciers.

Glaciers quarry the rock at their heads. Summer meltwater seeps into fractures in rock adjacent to the ice. The water expands when it freezes and breaks out fragments of the rock, which become incorporated in ice against the headwall and are carried down and away when the ice begins to flow. Gradually through successive periods of glaciation the great cliffed basins, called cirques, have been quarried into the flat-topped uplands. A glacier flowing down a valley also quarries rock at

Cirques at head of Glacier Basin. From left to right Taylor, Andrews, Chaos, and Tyndall (photo in February 1973). (Fig. 18)

places where there are numerous deep cracks in the bedrock. Meltwater or flowing ice penetrates the cracks and breaks out fragments which are drawn out into the glacier. In this way, glaciers eventually quarry ledges and even high cliffs, called giant stairs, along valley floors.

Glaciers abrade the rocks over which they flow. Stones, sand, and finer material held in the bottom of the ice grind against the underlying bedrock, rasping away silt-size particles, called rock flour, that give many glacial streams and lakes their milky, greenish, or pale-blue color. Small lakes, called tarns, common to many cirques and valley floors, lie in basins scoured into bedrock by this process. In like manner, glaciers flowing over bedrock knobs abrade them to streamlined shapes of least resistance to flowing ice. Glaciers also polish and groove the bedrock surfaces over which they pass. Many such surfaces are marked by small, closely spaced parallel scratches, called striations. Stones carried within a glacier are also rounded, faceted, and scratched by abrasion against

Glacially scoured and polished rock knobs south of Bear Lake parking area. (Fig. 19)

each other or against bedrock. Though abrasion produces many spectacular phenomena, it does not seem to account for deep glacial erosion. Quarrying and shearing are the major ways in which glaciers erode deeply into bedrock.

Glaciers deposit the rock debris they carry, either at the edge of the ice or under it. The debris slides or is dropped from the edge of a glacier where it gradually builds up a ridge. Such a ridge at the side of a glacier is called a lateral moraine; if at the end, an end moraine. The pushing and shearing of the ice at the snout of a glacier helps to build up end moraines. Rock debris dropped or sheared from beneath a glacier is called ground moraine. At the edge of an advancing glacier the material of moraines is continuously being picked up and deposited again, but as the glacier recedes from the farthest position of any advance it leaves its lateral and end moraines behind.

Early Glacial And Interglacial Times

The most ancient glacial deposits in the Rocky Mountains, known only from a single locality in Yellowstone National Park, are about 1.6 million years old. Deposits of at least two younger early glaciations, both older than 600,000 years, have been recognized in several mountain areas. Such deposits are difficult to find and identify, for most have been stripped away by later glaciers. As yet, no record of any of the early glaciers has been found in Rocky Mountain National Park. However, from what is known about them in other mountains they probably extended down the canyons in the Park about as far as did the younger glaciers.

Each of the early glaciations was separated from its successor by an interglacial period during which no glaciers existed. In Glacier National Park and elsewhere in the Rocky Mountains, the deposits of early glaciations have been found one above the other in sequence. Each deposit is separated from its successor by an unusually thick soil, which required a long period of interglacial weathering in which to form. The last of the early glaciations ended about 600,000 years ago. Toward the end of the long interglacial period following it, streams deepened the canyons about 200 feet along the eastern margin of the Front Range before the advance of the oldest intermediate glaciers.

A mammoth of the Ice Age.

The Intermediate Glaciers

Glaciers intermediate between the early glaciers and the last great glaciers may have advanced down the canyons and then wasted away completely several times between about 500,000 years ago and about 87,000 years ago, but deposits of only the last two of these intermediate glaciers are known in the Park. The glacial times were separated by interglacial times about which little is known. They may have been colder, warmer, wetter, or drier than today.

The oldest of the intermediate glaciations known in the Park probably occurred about 160,000 years ago. Its deposits can be seen in roadcuts along Colorado Highway 7 in the southern part of Tahosa Valley, near the eastern boundary of the Park. They consist of reddish-yellow unsorted silty sand, small angular pieces of disintegrated gneiss, scattered dark and light round pebbles and cobbles, and a few boulders. Some of the dark, hard stones bear the scratches of the glacier which carried them from the area of Longs Peak. The boulders have crumbly surfaces and tend to be broken. The deposits are only 1 to 6 feet thick, and overlie yellowish, deeply disintegrated gneiss bedrock. Any end moraines which they may once have formed have been destroyed by the years. The reddish color and decayed character are due to weathering since the recession of the oldest known intermediate glaciers.

Similar old intermediate glacial deposits have been found east of the Fall River entrance to the Park, at the lower end of the straight, broadly U-shaped stretch of the valley of Fall River just above the canyon leading to Estes Park. These deposits mark the maximum extent of glaciation in the valley as shown by the fact that the canyon immediately downstream is a narrow, sinuous, V-shaped stream-cut gorge in deeply weathered rocks that show no evidence of ever having been glaciated.

The younger intermediate glaciation, called the Bull Lake Glaciation, consists of two advances separated by a major withdrawal of the ice. The early Bull Lake advance probably began after about 127,000 years ago and ended about 105,000 years ago. The late Bull Lake advance probably began after about 100,000 years ago. It may have ended about 87,000 years ago but was certainly completed before about 70,000 years ago. These two glacial advances were much alike. Their glaciers stemmed from the same cirques, extended down the same canyons, and joined with tributary glaciers to form large rivers of ice in the same major valleys. At both times, the glaciers were as much as 2,000 feet thick in the upper canyons, and their lower ends extended beyond the boundaries of the Park. Here they left behind end moraines and lateral moraines, the principal deposits of these two glacial advances remaining today.

The end moraines of the early and late Bull Lake glaciers are similar in appearance. Both are broad, smooth ridges. Where they cross major valleys they have been widely breached by later stream erosion. The moraines are composed of pale-brown compact silty sand containing stones of many sizes, shapes, and rock types. A few of the hard stones still show glacial scratches. The weathered zone, or soil, at the surface of both moraines is brown to reddish brown, compact, silty, and 3 to 4 feet deep. This weathering is much less intensive and less deep than that of the oldest intermediate glacial deposits. Boulders are not abundant on the surface of the moraines, and tend to be broken or to have crumbly outer rinds.

The end moraines of the early Bull Lake advance usually lie only a short distance downstream from those of the late advance. In view of their similarities, it is logical to ask, "Why don't these two moraines simply represent two minor pulsations of a single glacial advance?" They don't because in several places in the Rocky Mountains deposits of the late Bull Lake advance overlie conspiciously weathered deposits of the early Bull Lake advance. The presence of the weathered zone, or soil, between the two glacial deposits denotes a considerable time of glacial recession and perhaps nearly complete disappearance of the ice. The two end moraines therefore, must represent two distinctly separate major glacial advances.

End moraines of the early and late Bull Lake glaciers can be seen in a number of places near the Park boundaries. In the valley of Fall River, just east of the Park entrance, the highway crosses two low, bouldery ridges. The outer is the end moraine of the early Bull Lake glacier and the inner is the end moraine of the late glacier. The outer moraine descends from above the highway into the valley at about the position of the Water Plant and swings back upstream along the ridge on the south side of the valley. The inner moraine descends into the valley just outside the Park boundary and swings back up the south side of the valley through Aspenglen Campground. It is easily seen in the lower part of the campground, where it overlies a bedrock ridge that projects in places from beneath it. The brownish, compact, silty deposit containing both stained and disintegrated stones contrasts markedly with the pale-gray, sand deposit, containing fresh gray stones, of the large end moraine of the last glaciation immediately upstream.

Bull Lake end moraine along Glacier Creek in Tuxedo Park. Boulders are cracked or broken and preserve little of their original glacially abraded surface. (Fig. 20)

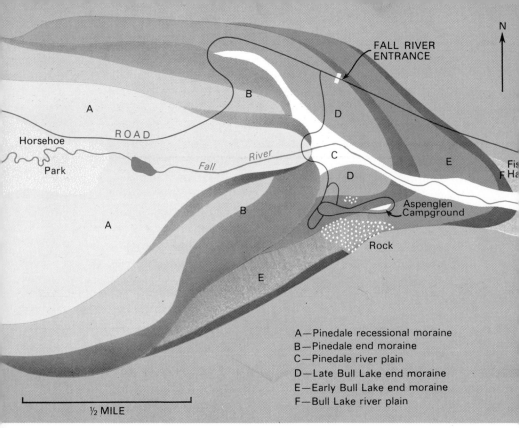

A—Pinedale recessional moraine
B—Pinedale end moraine
C—Pinedale river plain
D—Late Bull Lake end moraine
E—Early Bull Lake end moraine
F—Bull Lake river plain

Map of Bull Lake and Pinedale moraines in area of Aspenglen Campground.

A moraine of the early Bull Lake advance is crossed by the highway just west of the Beaver Meadows entrance to the Park. It is a broad, low, smooth, pine-covered ridge, about 40 feet high, that is sparsely littered with large and small, more or less weathered and broken boulders. Beyond, to the west, the highway follows the south side of the moraine and then turns and crosses it again to ascend Deer Ridge. The brownish, compact soil on the glacial deposit can be seen in the shallow roadcuts, and careful examination of hard, dark stones will reveal glacial scratches on some of them. This end moraine was deposited by an early Bull Lake glacier which flowed down the valley of Big Thompson River through Moraine Park. It is now separated from that valley by a high forested ridge, a moraine of the last glaciation. The moraine of the late Bull Lake advance, which should normally be between these two moraines, probably is buried beneath the high moraine of the last glaciation. This may account for its unusual size.

On the west side of the Park, Bull Lake glaciers descended the valley of the Colorado River and deposited broad, smooth end moraines south of Shadow Mountain Lake. The end moraine of the early Bull Lake advance is crossed by the highway between that lake and Lake Granby. The end moraine of the late Bull Lake advance encircles the southernmost end of the Shadow Mountain Lake. These glacial deposits are similar to those in the eastern part of the Park, except that they contain large quantities of volcanic rock brought down the valley by the glaciers from the Never Summer Mountains.

A Time in Question

There is as yet no record of what happened in Rocky Mountain National Park from the end of the Bull Lake Glaciation to the beginning of the last glaciation. However, studies in progress of plant and tree pollen obtained from sediments of this interval in other areas show changes in the local vegetation of those areas that reflect broad changes in climate. These climatic changes probably were sufficient to have affected the Park. They suggest that the time of retreat and disappearance of the late Bull Lake glaciers, possibly about 87,000 years ago

ine-covered early Bull Lake end moraine in Beaver Meadows. Moraines of last glaciation (Pine-
ale) lie in forest to lower left. (Fig. 21)

and certainly before 70,000 years ago, was followed by a warm interval, somewhat like today. Then, about 70,000 years ago, the climate turned markedly colder, and glaciers may have advanced again about 45,000 years ago. If so, they probably receded about 32,000 years ago when the climate warmed again. Finally, perhaps about 27,000 years ago, the cold climate, which led to the beginning of the last widespread glaciation, set in.

The Last Glaciation

Cooling of the climate at the beginning of the last glaciation caused snowline to be lowered again. Present snowline (the average lower limit of névé in late summer) in the Park is at about 11,800 feet. This is halfway between the average altitude of the lower ends of the present glaciers (11,100 feet) and the average altitude of the crests of the cirque headwalls (12,500 feet). The average altitude of the outermost end moraines of the last glaciation is about 8,270 feet. The average altitude of the crests of cirque headwalls during the last glaciation was the same as now (12,500 feet). A point halfway be-

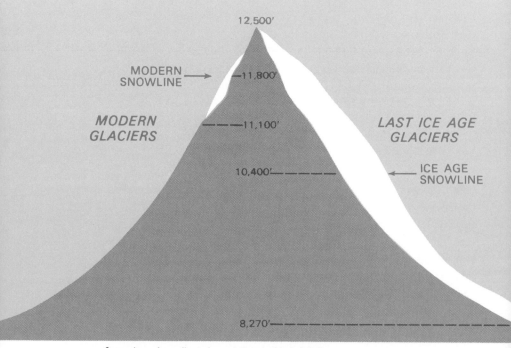

Comparison of snowline today and at peak of last glaciation.

47

Head of valley of Cache La Poudre River through which ice overflowed from the Colorado River. View from Trail Ridge Road. (Fig. 22)

tween, at 10,400 feet, is a reasonable estimate of the altitude of snowline in the Park during the maximum extent of the last great glaciers, and is about 1,400 feet lower than present snowline. This does not mean that perennial snow lay everywhere above 10,400 feet, but only that it lay above this altitude on the glaciers and in places so sheltered that it did not melt in summer.

The glaciers formed in most of the same cirques as did the Bull Lake glaciers. From these basins, they advanced down the canyons, and may have attained their maximum length about 15,000 years ago.

This last of the major glaciations of the Ice Age is called the Pinedale Glaciation. A glance at the map will show the extent of the ice in and around Rocky Mountain National Park. On the east side of the mountains, glaciers stemmed from groups of cirques along the Continental Divide and in the Mummy Range. They flowed as tongues, mostly 8 to 10 miles long, down each major valley. The longest, about 13 miles long, was in the valley of Big Thompson River. The snouts of the glaciers rose abruptly 200 to 300 feet. In the upper parts of the canyons, the ice was 1,000 to 1,500 feet thick.

On the west side of the mountains, névé fields lay along the entire length of the Continental Divide and also on the high ridges to the west. As a result, the glaciers were nourished not only from their heads but also from their sides, and built up to such a thickness that they overflowed across the ridges in many places to form a complex network of ice streams. Some of these glaciers were over 1,500 feet thick.

Extent of glaciers in Rocky Mountain National Park and adjacent Front Range during the Pinedale Glaciation. Greater extent of preceding Bull Lake glaciers, where known, is shown by dotted lines

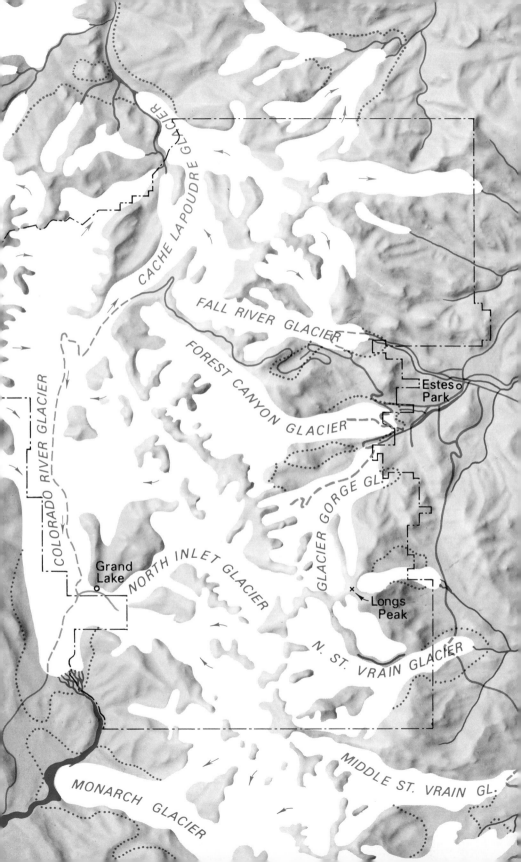

CACHE LAPOUDRE GLACIER

FALL RIVER GLACIER

FOREST CANYON GLACIER

COLORADO RIVER GLACIER

Estes
Park

GLACIER GORGE GL.

Grand
Lake

NORTH INLET GLACIER

× Longs
Peak

N. ST. VRAIN GLACIER

MIDDLE ST. VRAIN GL.

MONARCH GLACIER

In the northwest part of the Park, glaciers formed in cirques along the crest of the Never Summer Mountains. They flowed eastward to the valley of the Colorado River where they merged with glaciers flowing westward from the Continental Divide to form the largest glacier in the Park. This great river of ice, from its head west of La Poudre Pass to its terminus at the chain of islands across Shadow Mountain Lake, was 20 miles long, the longest in the Park. Its headward part overflowed eastward across Milner Pass into the valley of the Cache la Poudre River.

Much of the scenic beauty of the Park today is the work of the last great glaciers. The cirque basins were originally roughed out by the early and intermediate glaciers. However, the steep headwalls along the Continental Divide as seen from Trail Ridge Road, or the awe-inspiring east face of Longs Peak as viewed by a climber at Chasm Lake, were steepened, deepened, and brought to their present rugged condition by the quarrying action of the last glaciers. The beautiful tarns

U-shaped glaciated canyon of Fall River above Horseshoe Park. (Fig. 23)

Chain Lakes. Fourth, Spirit, and Verna Lakes, scoured by ice in bedrock of upper canyon of East Inlet; view from Tanina Peak. (Fig. 24)

within the cirques, such as Chasm Lake, or Frozen Lake at the head of Glacier Gorge, were scoured from bedrock by stones frozen and dragged along in the bottom of the glaciers.

Below the cirques, the great U-shaped canyons, such as the canyon of Fall River above Horseshoe Park, or Hayden Gorge, or Tyndall Gorge, so often photographed with Hallett Peak from Dream Lake, were deepened, steepened, and scoured by the last glaciers — though, like the cirques, they had been shaped by earlier glaciers. In places, the upper limit of glacial polish and other scour features high on the canyon walls show approximately where the surface of the ice lay. Above, jagged and fractured cliffs rise to the rim of the gently sloping uplands.

The ice both quarried and polished the canyon floors. Over the cliffed fronts of giant rock stairs, some more than 200 feet high, the glaciers flowed, broken at their surfaces by a maze of crevasses. At the bottom of the glaciers, ice or water penetrated fractures in the rock, loosening blocks and quarrying them from the cliff faces.

Below the cliffs the full abrasive force of stone-laden ice was brought to bear on the valley floor, scouring depressions now filled with water and linked together by streams to form a chain of lakes. Gorge Lakes, as seen from Trail Ridge, are typical, as are Emerald and Dream Lakes below Tyndall gorge and Sky Pond, Glass Lake, and others.

Elsewhere along the valleys the glaciers abraded large rock knobs, such as Glacier Knobs below Glacier Gorge, smoothing and shaping them into stream-lined forms. Smaller rounded and smoothed knobs and ledges abound along the valleys, especially near and above timberline where there is little soil or forest cover. When seen from a distance a group of these knobs resembles the backs of scattered sheep, from which their name, "roches moutonées," is derived.

Shallow glacial grooves showing the direction of local down-valley ice movement many be found on smooth slopes, rock ledges, and knobs in the upper valleys. Here also, glacial striations, the fine parallel scratches abraded on rock by stones and sand held in the base of a glacier, can be found. They too record the direction of ice movement of the last glaciers. Many rock surfaces have also been polished by sand and silt in the overriding ice. These features are less commonly found in the

53

Glacially striated rock surface about 100 yards above second switchback of road up the canyon of Fall River. Arrow points at knife for scale. (Fig. 25)

lower valleys because the soil and forest cover is more widespread, and because many have been removed by weathering of the bedrock. Some, easily seen, are along the one-way road up the canyon of Fall River, about 100 yards above the second switchback, where construction of the road has stripped away the soil mantle to expose the fresh, bare, grooved, striated and polished bedrock of the valley wall.

The lower ends of some U-shaped canyons lie above the floors of main valleys, into which their streams descend in a series of cascades or falls. The valleys of Roaring River, Chiquita Creek, and Sundance Creek, all tributary to Fall River in Horseshoe Park, are examples. Such valleys, called hanging valleys, are believed to result from undercutting of the tributary valley by the greater eroding power of the main valley glacier. Though this is true in regions where glaciers were a few thousand feet thick, undercutting of the hanging valley of Chiquita and Sundance Creeks as much as 500 feet by a glacier at most only 800 feet thick in this part of the valley of Fall River during the last glaciation would not have been possible. Such undercutting, if of glacial origin, must have been accomplished by thicker ice during an earlier glaciation.

54

Glacial basin of Moraine Park bordered by large moraines of last glaciation (Pinedale). Helicopter view from southeast. (Fig. 26)

Most of the glaciers reached their outer limits in the lower valleys just inside the Park boundaries. Along these gentle slopes the solid ice fronts of the glaciers were shoved forward by the force of flowing ice behind. This thrusting from the rear caused the solid ice to break and shear up over itself, dragging up with it quantities of rock debris from beneath. The large basins of Horseshoe Park, Moraine Park, Glacier Basin, and Shadow Mountain Lake were excavated in this way.

The deposits of the last, or Pinedale Glaciation, cover the valley floors and form prominent, forested, end moraines and lateral moraines. These are large ridges, littered with numerous light-gray boulders. The end moraines loop around the lower ends of the valley basins. Lateral moraines extend from them upstream along both valley walls. The deposits are a loose mixture of sand and stones of many kinds, both large and small. The stones are mostly unbroken and unweathered. Few display glacial striations. The deposits have only a thin pale-yellow soil, or zone of weathering. Their surfaces are commonly hummocky, in places enclosing depressions and small ponds. On the whole, they look much fresher than deposits of the Bull Lake glaciers.

Bouldery Pinedale end moraines along Fall River above Aspenglen Campground. (Fig. 27)

Bouldery deposit of Pinedale lateral moraine along road to Adams Falls east of Grand Lake. (Fig. 28)

In the valley of Fall River, the Pinedale end moraine is the high bouldery ridge over which the highway passes, west of the Park entrance. From the upper end of Horseshoe Park the highway ascends the south side of the valley to Many Parks Curve through the south lateral moraine, whose contact with the deeply weathered gneiss of the valley wall is well displayed along the road. From turnouts and from Many Parks Curve you can see the north lateral moraine on the rim across the valley. Higher up, the road follows the inner edge of the south lateral moraine ridge which crosses the mouth of Hidden Valley, showing thereby that no glacier existed in that valley in Pinedale time.

There is no prominent end moraine at the lower end of Moraine Park, though boulders were deposited by the Pinedale ice as much as 220 feet above the Visitor Center on the slope of Eagle Cliff Mountain. High lateral moraines rising above both sides of the valley can be seen from the Visitor Center. As mentioned, their great size may be because they overlie Bull Lake moraines.

End moraine of Pinedale glacier in valley of Fall River. In foreground, the moraine blocks the mouth of Hidden Valley, which was not occupied by a glacier at that time. (Fig. 29)

Pinedale terminal moraine forming islands in Shadow Mountain Lake, a modern reservoir. View looking north from early Bull Lake moraine at foot of lake. (Fig. 30)

The end moraine of the Pinedale glacier in Glacier Basin is crossed where the road ascends to the basin. From the campground, a magnificent panorama clearly shows the high lateral moraines of the last glaciation extending far up both sides of the valley. Should you climb to Bierstadt Lake, you can see that the lake is enclosed between the Pinedale lateral moraine and an older-looking lateral moraine of Bull Lake age which forms the higher ridge to the north.

In the lower part of the steep valley east of Longs Peak, the Pinedale end moraine breaches the end moraines of the Bull Lake glaciers and extends nearly to the highway.

On the west side of the mountains, the end moraine of the Pinedale glacier in the valley of the Colorado River forms the peninsulars and islands that trend across the lower part of Shadow Mountain Lake. This artificial lake is dammed in the large basin excavated by the lower end of the glacier.

58

Above And Beyond The Ice

While the glaciers were at their maximum extent, the ice nearly filled the canyons to their rims. Above, the uplands were probably blown nearly clear of snow in winter, though deep drifts accumulated on lee slopes. These drifts lasted well into the summer, in places possibly throughout the year, though they never became thick enough to form glaciers. Permafrost, or permanently frozen ground, probably formed where the snow cover failed to insulate the uplands. As the climate began to warm and the ice began its retreat, meltwater from the snow and permafrost penetrated fractures in the rock. Here, successive freezing and thawing broke up the rock and mixed with

Mantle of angular blocks and sandy debris on the gently sloping summit upland of Bighorn Flats, at 11,600 feet near Sprague Pass. (Fig. 31)

Exposure of the blocky upland mantle along Trail Ridge Road. (Fig. 32)

Patterned ground formed by frost-sorting of angular stones in blocky mantle on the north side of Trail Ridge Road east of Rock Cut. (Fig. 33)

the overlying soil to form the mantle of angular blocks and sandy debris that is so characteristic of the uplands today. Frost heave tilted many slabs upward and, on gentle slopes, formed patterns in the ground. On steeper slopes, gravity caused the debris to slide downhill, giving the slopes a wavy expression or downhill streaming. Most of these deposits are now stable and overgrown with tundra, through which the blocks project.

In places, thawing ground and snow meltwater so fully saturated the stony slope deposits that they flowed slowly downhill. Examples of such solifluction (soil flowage) are widespread on Trail Ridge. Large bouldery solifluction terraces bench the slope of Sundance Mountain east of Forest Canyon Overlook. Smaller, less bouldery terraces form low treads on the slopes along Trail Ridge Road south of Iceberg Lake. Solifluction lobes occur below the road east of Rock Cut.

Bouldery solifluction terraces on slope of Sundance Mountain east of Forest Canyon Overlook. (Fig. 34)

Active solifluction terrace below Trail Ridge Road east of Rock Cut. Note springs, ponds, and hummocks at back of terrace; frost boils on outer edge. (Fig. 35)

Soil flowage is no longer active over most of the uplands. However, here and there in the wetter places, frost heave, thaw, and soil flowage still go on today on a small scale. Some features of this activity are both curious and interesting. Many are to be seen near Trail Ridge Road. An active solifluction terrace lies on the slope below the road just east of Rock Cut. A group of irregular circles or polygons of stone slabs with centers of sandy material occur along the north side of the large curve east of Rock Cut, in the wet ground at the foot of a melting snowbank. The sorting process by which the slabs are separated from the sand actively goes on each summer.

Along the trail over the upland west of Iceberg Lake is a network of stone-filled channels a few feet wide in which the stones have been concentrated by frost heave and thaw from underlying and adjacent material containing both sand and stones. Narrow stone-filled channels, called block streams, can be seen from Iceberg Lake on the slopes of the upland to the north.

Low rounded hills in the basin south of Fall River Pass are patterned by a series of closely spaced narrow treads that angle diagonally across their slopes like parallel trails. These are not made by animals, but rather by the slow flow of material directed laterally down the slope by tundra vegetation growing on the steep fronts of the treads — hence their name, turf-banked terraces. On the flatter tops of the hills active frost heave has formed a closely spaced pattern of circles, or "frost boils," in which the vegetation cannot get a foothold. Where the slopes steepen, these circular areas of frost activity flow together to form turf-banked terraces.

In valleys below the limits of the glaciers, the colder climate also induced frost heave and downslope movement of slope debris. Where there were cliffs of hard rock, freezing and thawing of moisture in the cracks pried loose blocks. These fell and accumulated at the base of the cliffs as cones or sheets of angular rock debris, called talus. Where the rock had been deeply weathered in preglacial time, as around Estes Park, soil flow at times of thaw stripped away the soft weathered sandy debris, leaving behind round, hard rock cores as giant boulders. These either remained behind in precariously balanced positions on the hills or tumbled down the slopes. They are abundant on the hills at the northeast edge of Estes Park and along the road north of town.

Active sorted polygons east of Rock Cut. Rock slabs in water are sorted from central sandy areas by frost heave and thaw. (Fig. 36)

Network of stone-filled channels separated by frost action from central grassy areas of stones mixed with sand. On widespread upland above Iceberg Lake. (Fig. 37)

Channel filled with blocks separated by frost action from intervening grass-covered areas of blocks mixed with sand. On slope north of Iceberg Lake. (Fig. 38)

Turf-banked terraces in basin south of Fall River Pass. (Fig. 39)

Balanced boulders, remaining after deeply weathered rock has been stripped away. On hills northeast of Estes Park. (Fig. 40)

Under the cold conditions that existed during the advance of the glaciers, the forests retreated downslope and a widespread tundra extended to altitudes perhaps as low as 8,000 feet. East of the mountains the forest spread far out on the High Plains where it became the habitat of mammoths, wooly rhinoceros, bison, and other large mammals.

. . . And Sudden Death

Amelioration of the climate and the beginning of glacial recession probably set in about 13,000 years ago. The glaciers did not retreat continuously at first, but pulsated back and forth across short distances, leaving behind one or more recessional moraines. During one of these minor readvances in the valley of Fall River, a small glacier tongue pushed through the outermost end moraine and left a narrow hairpin-shaped moraine which extends through the outer moraine nearly to the Aspenglen Campground. In Glacier Basin, meltwaters flowing along the edge of the ice built a great gravel terrace at the site of Glacier Basin Campground. Later, minor readvances of the glacier constructed two small moraines across the valley above the basin. West of the mountains, the large moraine which encloses Grand Lake was built by a readvance of the glacier in the canyon of East Inlet. A highway cut through the moraine at one time showed that the moraine overlies layers of soft silt deposited in a lake into which the ice readvanced.

65

Moraine of a readvance of the last glaciation (Pinedale) enclosing Grand Lake, to the left, and bordered to the right by Shadow Mountain Lake, a reservoir. Distant islands in Shadow Mountain Lake form terminal moraine of maximum advance of the last glaciation (Pinedale). (Fig. 41)

Once the recession really set in, the ice wasted rapidly, and glaciers several miles long and 1,500 feet thick nearly disappeared in less than 1,000 years. During this time meltwaters flowed downvalley from the ice in much greater volume than during the glacial advance. Large lakes existed in Horseshoe Park, Glacier Basin, and in the valley of the Colorado River north of the Park entrance. Moraine Park may have contained a shallow lake, though this is not certain. Soon, however, the heavily laden glacial streams filled the lakes with sand and gravel until they became mere swampy flats. Only Grand Lake survived.

Attempts at Revival

By about 12,000 years ago, the glaciers had retreated to the valley heads. Shortly thereafter, the forest spread rapidly back into the mountains. A little more than 11,000 years ago, man made his way into the region from Alaska. Folsom and Yuma Points attest his presence in many places in Colorado; among them, the archaeologically famous Lindenmeier Site on the plains east of the mountains near the Wyoming State line. Curiously, the large mammals of the Ice Age, excepting the bison, died out coincidently. Man may have played a part in their extinction!

66

Layered lake sediments of lake overrun by moraine of Pinedale readvance that encloses Grand Lake. Formerly exposed along highway west of Grand Lake village. (Fig. 42)

Brief cold periods at different times between 11,000 and 8,000 years ago induced a succession of minor readvances of the glaciers which left at least two small moraines in many of the upper valleys. These are low ridges, usually covered with large blocks. Most are forested. The Loch Vale Trail crosses a lateral moraine formed by one of these advances in a burned area about half a mile west of the Trail head, and follows the crest of another just above Alberta Falls. The forested moraine enclosing Fern Lake was also formed by one of these advances. Finally, however, the glaciers receded into the cirques and, about 7,500 years ago, disappeared entirely.

A Warm Dry Time

From about 7,500 years ago to about 3,800 years ago, snowline was above the summits and the climate was at times warmer than today. Treeline was higher and summers were probably somewhat longer. Blocks fell less frequently from the cliffs; movement of debris was rare on summit uplands. Slopes became stable under the protective cover of vegetation. Erosion was minimal in the mountains.

During this time paleo-Indians penetrated the region of the Park in summer in search of game. Possibly it was these people who first developed the Ute Trail, named for its use by a much later tribe from west of the mountains.

Glaciers Reborn

About 3,800 years ago the climate cooled again. Snow accumulated in the cirques, and small glaciers formed and began to move outward from the shelter of the headwalls into the cirque basins. These little glaciers were never more than half a mile long. Their end moraines are mostly in the cirque basins or just below them. The moraines are fresh and very bouldery. Stones in them show but little glacial wear because they were not carried far by the ice. Three and locally four such moraines are present in the most protected cirques, those facing north or northeast. The outermost two of the four have a thin soil cover that supports a grassy tundra vegetation. The third has almost no soil, but a few sparse pioneer plants grow on them, especially on their down-valley slopes. The innermost are fresh, with no soil or plant cover. Lichens are more abundant on the surface of boulders on the outer moraines than on the intermediate, and are very sparse or lacking on the inner. The size of individual lichen on the boulders and Carbon-14 dates of organic debris in the deposits tell us that these moraines were formed by small advances of the glaciers at different times. One of the two older moraines, and possibly both,

Very bouldery moraine of late readvance of last glaciation below Alberta Falls. View from Bear Lake parking area. (Fig. 43)

formed between 3,800 and 2,550 years ago; the third formed
between 1,850 and 950 years ago (100 A.D. - 1000 A.D.); and
the youngest formed during the last 300 years, chiefly about
100 years ago (1870 A.D.). This period, from 3,800 years ago to
the present, is called the Little Ice Age or Neoglaciation.

The moraines can be seen only by climbing into the cirques
or looking down into them from the Continental Divide. Among
the most accessible are those below Andrews Glacier, Taylor
Glacier, Chiefshead Glacier, and Mills Glacier. In some places,
the little glaciers were so heavily laden with debris from the
cliffs at their heads that, when the ice melted, a lobate glacier-
shaped mass of rock debris was left behind. Such deposits are
called rock glaciers. The deposits at the foot of Tyndall Glacier and Taylor Glacier are rock glaciers.

The Glaciers Today

The glaciers in the Park today are remnant from the last
expansion of the small glaciers which began to develop in empty
cirques about 3,800 years ago. They are not relics of the glaciers of the Ice Age and are as different from them as they are
from the large modern glaciers in Alaska. Some, in fact, may
be only 300 years old, for they may have disappeared briefly
during the dry years of the 11th and 12th centuries and re-

Two moraines of the older glaciers of the Little Ice Age, probably formed between 3,800 and 2,550 years ago, at head of canyon of Spruce Creek. (Fig. 44)

Modern active ice-cored rock glacier below Tyndall glacier (1960). (Fig. 45)

Modern glaciers
a. Tyndall glacier (1963) (Fig. 46)
b. Rowe glacier (1952) (Fig. 47)
c. Sprague glacier (1950) (Fig. 48)
d. Moomaw glacier (1963), a small mass
   of stagnant ice and névé. (Fig. 49)

developed during the 18th century. Today, these glaciers are barely alive. All are in east- or north-facing cirques where snow accumulation and shelter from the sun are greatest. Few show any significant forward motion, though growth lines can be seen on most. A few are merely masses of ice that is no longer moving. Snowline, or the lower level of névé on the glaciers in summer, is within a few yards of the outer edge of the ice. This means that the formation of new ice each year is barely able to replace the annual loss by melting and evaporation. Though some glaciers still extend to their innermost end moraines, none are actively growing against them. Many glaciers have receded from their end moraines, leaving a basin occupied by a small pond. Though a few of these ponds are milky, showing that glacial silt is still being carried into them by glacial meltwater, most are sufficiently clear to suggest that the glacier is inactive. The most obvious sign of decay is the extent to which the glaciers have wasted away: Their lower ends are thin, their middle parts concave, and their upper parts shrunken. A broad band of whitish fresh rock, from which the ice has downwasted, stares from the base of cliffs around the glaciers. Many glaciers are less than 250 feet thick, meaning that the ice is no longer thick enough to flow. They are literally starving for nourishment.

Andrews Glacier is one of the few still active, due apparently to unusually strong drifting of snow across the Continental Divide at its head. Its profile is convex, it is more than 250 feet thick, and it shows some evidence of movement. But even Andrews Glacier is in a bare subsistence condition.

The most recent severe decay of the glaciers took place during the droughts of the 1930's. The upper parts of some glaciers are known to have thickened between 1947 and 1957, but no advance of the glacier snouts has been reported. It is surprising that they are able to exist at all, for they are among the most southerly in the Rocky Mountains and therefore most sensitive to changes in climate. Arapaho Glacier, at the head of the North Fork of Boulder Creek, just south of the Park, is the most southerly existing glacier. About 1,000 years ago, small glaciers probably existed in mountains as far south as Taos, New Mexico; about 3,000 years ago they existed in mountains as far south as Santa Fe.

a

b

c

Andrews Glacier through the years.
a. 1916 (Fig. 50)
b. 1929 (Fig. 51)
c. 1939 (Fig. 52)
d. 1949 (Fig. 53)
e. 1969 (Fig. 54)

d

e

And Tomorrow—?

The present interglacial period, that is, the time since the retreat of the last large glaciers in the mountains, has lasted about 12,000 years. Its warmest part was before the development of new small glaciers about 3,800 years ago. Scientists tell us that many of the interglacial periods which separated the major glacial advances of the ice age lasted from 10,000 to 15,000 years. Is another long cold period to be expected? Theoretically, this is possible, but positive signs are difficult to identify. Periods of a few years when winters have been harder than normal are well documented and remembered by older inhabitants; short periods when the climate has been warmer than normal, as during the 1930's, are remembered by many. Such short-term fluctuations in climate are normal and should not unduly concern us. Another long cold period may begin in a few millenia—or in a time about equivalent to that which has elapsed since the beginning of the Bronze Age. But until the small glaciers of today extend beyond their outermost moraines of 3,800 years ago in the high cirque basins, there would seem to be no cause for alarm. Of more significance to man would be a period of increased warmth and complete disappearance of the ice. A long-term drought could severely affect the semi-arid west. The small glaciers of the Park are very sensitive to climatic change. At present, they are barely holding their own.

Acknowledgments

Necessarily, this history has been based on the work of many geologists who have discussed their observations and conclusions in hundreds of technical articles published in a wide variety of scientific journals. A few of these reports are listed below. No overall geological treatise on the Park has ever been published and several parts of the Park have never been studied in detail. Fortunately the region outside the Park in Colorado and Wyoming is being intensively investigated at present, and I wish to thank specifically Norman M. Denson, Glenn A. Izett, Estella B. Leopold, G. Edward Lewis, Glenn R. Scott, Richard B. Taylor, and Donald E. Trimble for generously contributing their knowledge and ideas, and for helpful criticism of the manuscript. To Richard B. Taylor belongs credit for the discovery that Specimen Mountain and adjacent ridges are capped by an ashflow tuff and that they are not the remains of an extinct volcano; also that the volcanic rock filling the ancient valley at Iceberg Lake is ashflow tuff rather than a rhyolite flow, as had been thought. The ages of the glaciations and interglaciations of the Ice Age are determined from the relations of correlative glacial and interglacial deposits in Yellowstone National Park to volcanic rocks dated by J. D. Obradovich. The 1.6-million-year-old glacial deposit in Yellowstone National Park was found and its relations determined by K. L. Pierce. Richard G. Baker is studying the pollen from deposits in Yellowstone National Park on which statements about the climate of the last interglacial — **a time in question** — are based. Personnel of the National Park Service have assisted materially through providing photographs and editing and arranging publication, especially Dwight L. Hamilton, Chief Park Naturalist, Rocky Mountain National Park, and Wayne Alcorn, N.P.S. (retired), who took many of the photos. Special thanks go to my wife, Amelie Z. Richmond, for her patience and help in all phases of preparation of the manuscript.

Selected Additional Reading

Unfortunately, other than the two predecessors to this story, no non-technical geologic publications about the Park exist. The references below are all in professional journals, but can be understood by interested readers with elementary geologic knowledge. Several are about areas in southeastern Wyoming and central Colorado from which information has been drawn as a basis for this story.

Predecessors to This Story

Lee, W. T., 1917, The geologic story of Rocky Mountain National Park, Colorado: (Dept. Interior), U.S. Natl.' Park Service, 89 p.

Wegemann, C. H., 1961, A guide to the geology of Rocky Mountain National Park: National Park Service, 32 p.

Story of The Mountains

>1,800,000 to 530,000 years ago

Peterman, Z. E., Hedge, C. E., and Braddock, W. A., 1967, Age of Precambrian events in the northeastern Front Range, Colorado: Jour. Geophys. Research, v. 73, no. 6, p. 2277-2296.

Wahlstrom, E. E., 1956, Petrology and weathering of the Iron Dike, Boulder and Laramie Counties, Colorado: Geol. Soc. America Bull., v. 67, p. 147-163.

530,000,000 to 75,000,000 years ago

Finlay, G. I., 1916, Description of the Colorado Springs folio: U.S. Geol. Survey Folio no. 203.

Heaton, R. L., 1933, Ancestral Rockies and Mesozoic and late Paleozoic stratigraphy of Rocky Mountain Region: Amer. Assoc. Petrol. Geol. Bull., v. 17, no. 2, p. 109-168.

Walker, T. R., and Harmes, J. C., 1972, Eolian origin of flagstone beds, Lyons Sandstone (Permian), type area, Boulder Co., Colorado: Mountain Geologist, v. 9, nos. 2-3, p. 279-288.

Weimer, R. J., 1973, A guide to uppermost Cretaceous stratigraphy, Central Front Range, Colorado—Deltaic sedimentation, growth faulting and early Laramide crustal movement: Mountain Geologist, v. 10, no. 3, p. 53-97.

Weimer, R. J., and Land, C. B., Jr., 1972, Field guide to Dakota Group (Cretaceous) stratigraphy Golden-Morrison area, Colorado: Mountain Geologist, v. 9, nos. 2-3, p. 241-267.

75,000,000 to 2,000,000 years ago

Blackstone, D. L., Jr., 1974, Late Cretaceous and Cenozoic history of the Laramie Basin region southeast Wyoming: Geol. Soc. America. (In Press).

Corbett, M. K., 1966, The geology and structure of the Mt. Richthofen-Iron Mt. region, north-central Colorado: The Mountain Geologist, v. 3, p. 3-21.

Corbett, M. K., 1968, Tertiary volcanism of the Specimen-Lulu-Iron Mountain area, north-central Colorado, in Cenozoic volcanism in the Southern Rocky Mountains, R. C. Epis, ed.: Colorado School of Mines Quart., v. 63, no. 3, p. 1-37.

Epis, R. C., and Chapin, C. E., 1968, Geologic history of the Thirtynine mile volcanic field, central Colorado in Cenozoic volcanism in the Southern Rocky Mountains, R. C. Epis, ed.: Colorado School of Mines Quart., v. 63, no. 3, p. 51-85.

Epis, R. C., and Chapin, C. E., 1974, Geomorphic and tectonic implications of the post-Laramide, late Eocene erosion surface in the Southern Rocky Mountains: Geol. Soc. America. (In Press).

Knight, S. H., 1953, Summary of the Cenozoic history of the Medicine Bow Mountains, Wyoming, in Guidebook, Eighth Annual Field Conference, Laramie Basin, Wyo., and North Park, Colo.: Wyoming Geol. Assoc., p. 65-76.

Lee, W. T., 1922, Peneplains of the Front Range and Rocky Mountain National Park, Colorado: U.S. Geol. Survey Bull. 730 A, 17 p.

Leopold, E. B., and MacGinitie, H. D., 1972, Development and affinities of Tertiary floras in the Rocky Mountains—Floristics and paleofloristics of Asia and eastern North America, A. Graham, ed.: Elsevier Publishing Co., Amsterdam.

Scott, G. R., 1974, Tertiary surfaces and deposits of the Southern Rockies and their recognition: Geol. Soc. America Special Paper. (In Press).

Steven, T. A., 1956, Cenozoic geomorphic history of the Medicine Bow Mountains near the Northgate fluorspar district, Colorado: Colorado Sci. Soc. Proc., v. 17, no. 2, 55 p.

Taylor, R. B., Theobald, P. K., and Izett, G. A., 1968, Mid-Tertiary volcanism in the central Front Range, Colorado, in Cenozoic volcanism in the Southern Rocky Mountains, R. C. Epis, ed.: Colorado School of Mines Quart., v. 63, no. 3: p. 39-50.

Tweto, Ogden, 1974, Summary of Laramide orogeny in the Southern Rocky Mountains: Geol. Soc. America. (In Press).

Wahlstrom, E. E., 1940, Audubon-Albion stock, Boulder County, Colorado: Geol. Soc. America Bull., v. 51, p. 1789-1820.

Wahlstrom, E. E., 1947, Cenozoic physiographic history of the Front Range, Colorado: Geol. Soc. America Bull., v. 58, p. 551-572.

Wahlstrom, E. E., 1944, Structure and petrology of Specimen Mountain, Colorado: Geol. Soc. America Bull., v. 55, p. 77-90.

Story of The Ice Age

Benedict, J. B., 1968, Recent glacial history of an alpine area in the Colorado Front Range, U.S.A., II. Dating the glacial deposits: Jour. Glaciology, v. 7, p. 77-87.

Benedict, J. B., 1970, Downslope soil movement in a Colorado alpine region: rate, processes and climatic significance: Arctic and Alpine Research, v. 2, no. 3, p. 165-226.

Jones, W. D., and Quam, L. O., 1944, Glacial landforms in Rocky Mountain National Park: Jour. Geology, v. 52, p. 217-234.

Outcalt, S. I., 1965, The regimen of the Andrews Glacier in Rocky Mountain National Park, Colorado, 1957-1963: Water Resources Research, v. 1, no. 2, p. 277-282.

Outcalt, S. I., and MacPhail, D. D., 1965, A survey of Neoglaciation in the Front Range of Colorado: Colorado Univ. Studies, Ser. in Earth Sci., no. 4, 123 p.

Richmond, G. M., 1960, Glaciation of the east slope of Rocky Mountain National Park, Colorado: Geol. Soc. America Bull., v. 71, p. 1371-1382.

Richmond, G. M., 1965, Glaciation of the Rocky Mountains, in The Quaternary of the United States, H. E. Wright, Jr., and D. G. Frey, eds.: Princeton Univ. Press, p. 217-230.

Richmond, G. M., 1972, Appraisal of the future climate of the Holocene in the Rocky Mountains: Quaternary Research, v. 2, p. 315-322.

Rocky Mountain Nature Assoc., 1959, Glaciers in Rocky Mountain National Park: 15 p.

About The Author

Gerald M. Richmond, a native of Rhode Island, received his bachelor of arts degree from Brown University, his master of arts degree from Harvard University, and his doctor of philosophy degree from the University of Colorado. He began his studies of the Rocky Mountains in 1938, in the Wind River Range of Wyoming. Following a year of work in the Canal Zone, he joined the U.S. Geological Survey in 1942. He has resided in Denver since 1946. His field of research, the Ice Age in the Rocky Mountains, has included studies in Rocky Mountain, Glacier, and Yellowstone National Parks. His publications comprise more than 70 professional reports and maps. A year of research in the Alps in 1961 resulted in a paper comparing the glacial stratigraphy of the Alps and Rocky Mountains. In 1965, he received the Geological Society of America Kirk Bryan Award for a paper on the Quaternary Stratigraphy of the La Sal Mountains, Utah. He has served as president of the Colorado Scientific Society, and was elected an Honorary Life Member in 1971. He has also served as chairman of the Division of Geomorphology and Glacial Geology of the Geological Society of America, as Secretary-General of the VII Congress of the International Union for Quaternary Research, held in Boulder, Colorado, in 1965, and as president of that International Union from 1965 to 1969. He is a Fellow of the Geological Society of America and active in other scientific organizations. In 1969 he initiated the organization of the American Association for Quaternary Research.

ADMINISTRATION

Rocky Mountain National Park is administered by the National Park Service, U.S. Department of the Interior. A superintendent, whose address is Estes Park, Colo. 80517, is in immediate charge.

THE DEPARTMENT OF THE INTERIOR

As the Nation's principal conservation agency, the Department of the Interior has basic responsibilities for water, fish, wildlife, mineral, land, park, and recreational resources. Indian and Territorial affairs are other major concerns of America's "Department of Natural Resources." The Department works to assure the wisest choice in managing all our resources so each will make its full contribution to a better United States — now and in the future.

PRODUCTION CREDITS

Production Supervision: Artcraft Printers, Inc., Bozeman, Montana, U.S.A.

PHOTO CREDITS

BACK COVER: Hallet Peak viewed along Beirstadt Moraine